Row, Row, Row

W9-AWM-840

Each of these children has something in common with the two others in the same row of pictures. You can see that all three children in the top row across are wearing blue shirts. Look at the other rows across, down, and diagonally. Can you tell what's alike in each row?

Illustrated by John Nez

Answers on page 47.

LOST AND FOUND

It's been a very busy day at the Lost-and-Found Desk. Can you help the clerk return the lost items to their owners? Which item will be left on the shelf?

Answers on page 47.

Oh K!

How many things in this picture begin with the letter K?

Answers on page 47.

HIDDEN PLANETS

The names of all nine planets are hidden in the letters below. Can you find them? Look up, down, sideways, and diagonally. Be careful—some words overlap, and some are written backwards.

```
L M V E N U S O
R O E E A R T H
E S M R K A F P
T A O A C N L R
I T A P R U U R
P U P L T S R E
U R M O O O N Y
J N E P T U N E
```

Illustrated by Barbara Gray

WALKING WIGGLY

Mark is taking his new pet, Wiggly, for a walk. What do you think it is? Use your imagination, and finish this picture.

HOW MANY ___ IN A ___?

There are 60 s. in a m. That's a quick way to say 60 seconds in a minute. Now that you know the quick system, try these:

1. 3 f. in a y.

2. 7 d. in a w.

3. 4 q. in a g.

4. 12 m. in a y.

5. 12 i. in a f.

6. 2 c. in a p.

7. 60 m. in an h.

8. 365 d. in a y.

9. 24 h. in a d.

10. 52 w. in a y.

Illustrated by Jennifer Skopp

Answers on page 47.

CALL TO ORDER

These pictures are out of order. Can you number them so they tell a story from beginning to end?

Illustrated by John Nez

Answers on page 48.

PICTURE CROSSWORD

These pictures tell you what words to write in the spaces across → and down ↓.

SEE WHAT SUE SAW

Sue uses her binoculars wherever she goes. Can you tell where she went each day?

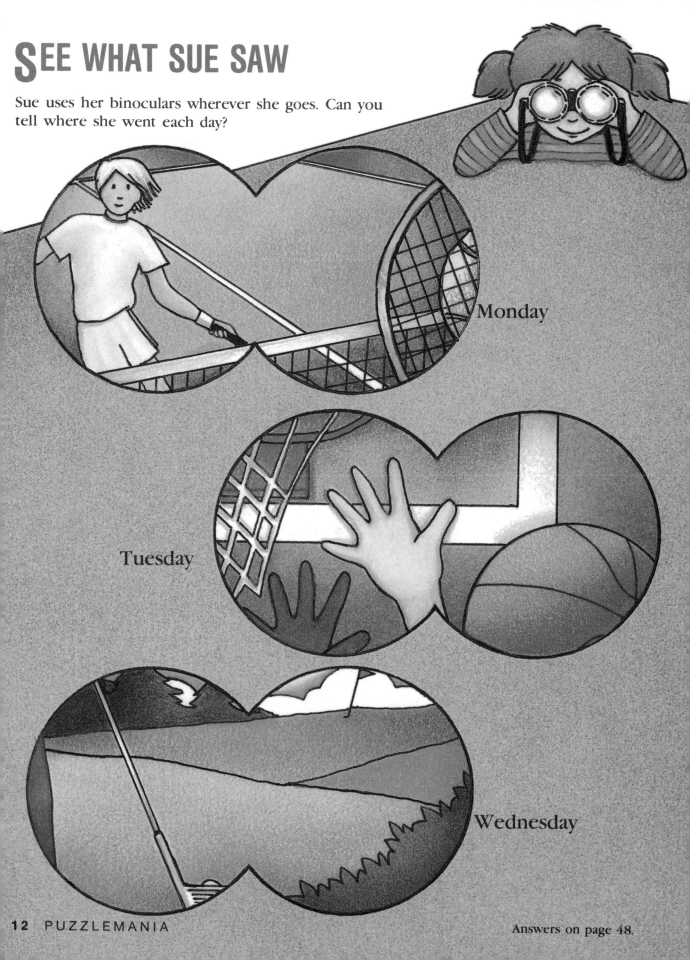

Monday

Tuesday

Wednesday

Answers on page 48.

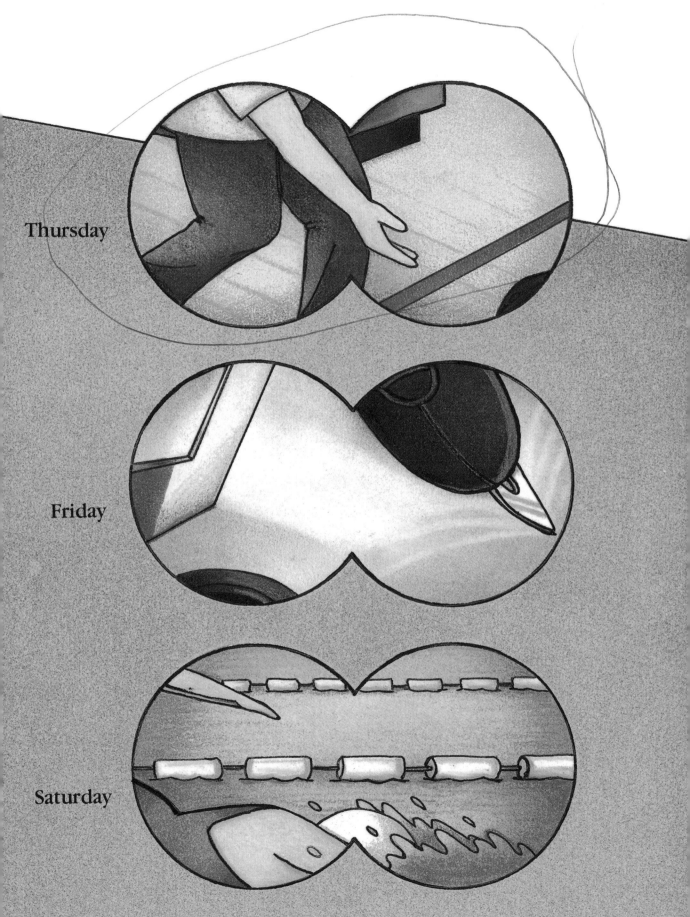

Thursday

Friday

Saturday

MIX-UP AT THE CANDY COMPANY

There's been a mix-up at Alexandra's Candy Company. The barrels are numbered, but no one knows what's in them. The letters on the labels have been scrambled. The one labeled MARASCLE is actually full of CARAMELS. Help Alexandra unscramble the other candy names so she can get back to pulling taffy.

1. MARASCLE — CARAMELS

2. FEOFET — TOFFEE

3. CILROCIE — LICORICE

4. MUGSPROD — GUMDROPS

5. LEJLY SNABE — Jelly Beans

6. LIPOSLOPL — LOLLIPOPS

7. SWALLOMSHARM — MARSHMALLOWS

8. HEATCLOCO — Chocolate

9. DUGEF — FUDGE

10. TENAPU TRIBLET — Peanut Brittle

Illustrated by Jerry Zimmerman

Answers on page 48.

HOP TO IT!

Harvey is hurrying home to his hutch. He needs to pick up groceries along the way. There are lots to choose from, but his family eats only raw vegetables. Which way should Harvey go to find foods that rabbits might like?

START

KOLA COLA

CANNED SOUP

HARVEY

FINISH

Illustrated by Barbara Gray

Answers on page 48.

ALPHABEADS

Start at the top with A. Move up, down, left, right, or diagonally to the nearest B. From there, move to the nearest C. Connect the beads to make an alphabet necklace from A to Z.

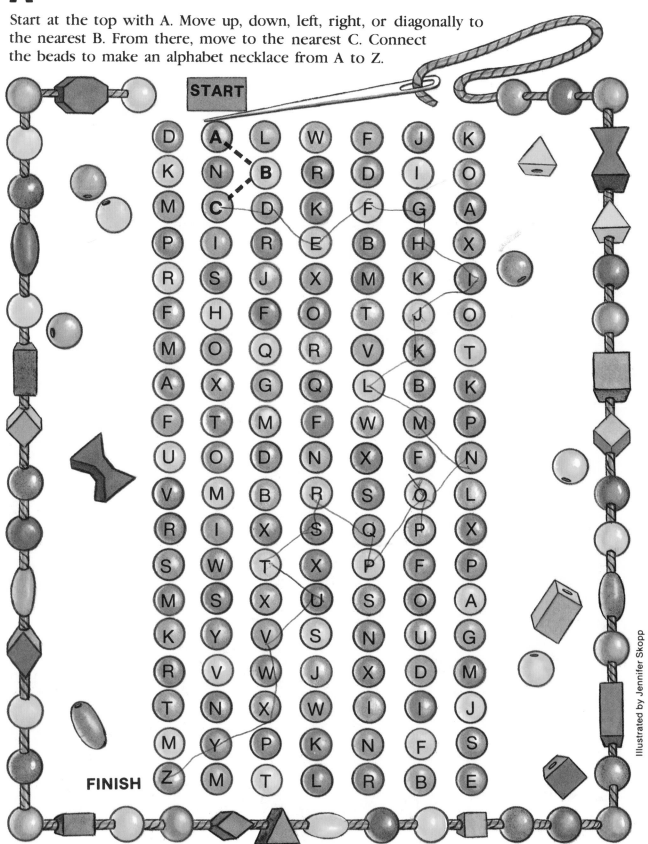

Illustrated by Jennifer Skopp

Answers on page 48.

JUNGLE MEMORIES
Part 1

Take a long look at this picture. Try to remember everything you see in it. Then turn the page and try to answer some questions about it without looking back.

DON'T READ THIS
UNTIL YOU HAVE
LOOKED AT
"Jungle Memories-Part 1"
ON PAGE 17

JUNGLE MEMORIES
Part 2

Can you answer these questions about the jungle scene you saw?

1. How many elephants did you see?
2. Was the turtle swimming?
3. Were all the animals right side up?
4. Did the cat have stripes or spots?
5. How many birds were on the vine?
6. Was the man holding an ice-cream cone or a cookie?
7. Which animal held a flower?
8. How many birds were flying?

Answers on page 48.

AT THE FINISH LINE

Pat, Emily, and Amy entered a Soap Box Derby. Each one took a prize. By reading the clues below, can you tell who took first, second, and third place? What color car did each one drive?

Pat beat only the blue car.

The yellow car was not first.

Amy was not driving the red car.

Answers on page 48.

WHAT HAVE WE HERE?

Where have you seen these shapes?
How many can you name?

Wiger

1.

2.

sartandpeper nif

3.

Meshingspoons

4.

roler

5.

steder   meishring cup   Hot pad

6.

7.

8.

Illustrated by Doug Taylor

TREASURE HUNT

Captain Richman keeps his treasure on a secret island. Starting at the ship, follow the directions on the map from island to island. When you find a letter, stash it away in the ship's locker. Once you reach Richman's Island, the letters will tell you what the captain keeps there.

Illustrated by Terry Kovalcik

SOMETHING FISHY

There are at least ten differences in these two pictures. How many can you find?

WHAT A WAY TO GO!

These explorers are traveling across the country. To find out how they'll get there, connect the red dots from 1 to 31. Then connect the blue dots from A to Z. Bon voyage!

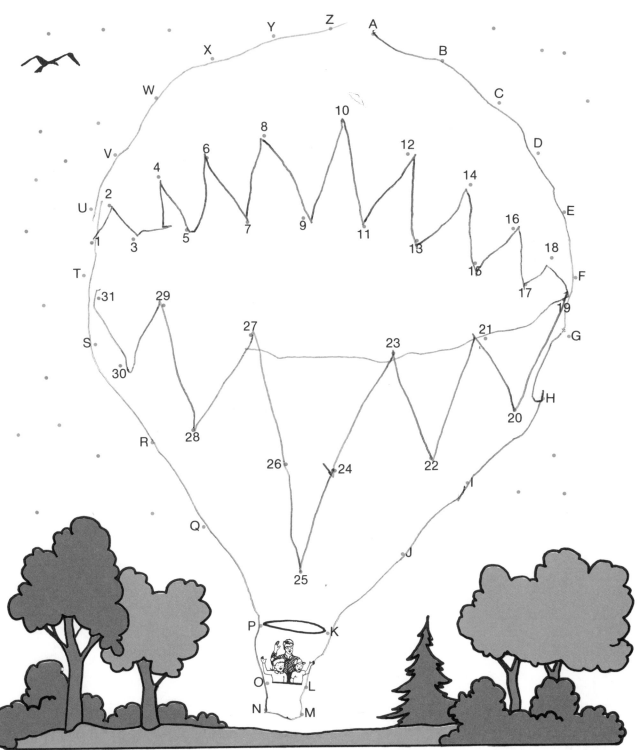

CROSSING THE STATES

The names of all fifty states fit into the spaces on the following page. The lists tell how many letters are in each state name. This will help you see where they fit into the puzzle. Some of the states have been filled in. It may help you to cross each state off the list when you put it in the puzzle.

4 LETTERS
Utah
Ohio
Iowa

5 LETTERS
Maine
Idaho
Texas

6 LETTERS
Nevada
Oregon
Alaska
Kansas
Hawaii

7 LETTERS
Montana
Arizona
Alabama
Indiana
Vermont
New York
Florida
Georgia
Wyoming

8 LETTERS
Oklahoma
Maryland
Colorado
Nebraska
Missouri
Illinois
Michigan
Virginia
Delaware
Kentucky
Arkansas

9 LETTERS
New Mexico
Louisiana
Wisconsin
Tennessee
Minnesota
New Jersey

10 LETTERS
California
Washington

11 LETTERS
South Dakota
North Dakota
Mississippi
Rhode Island
Connecticut

12 LETTERS
New Hampshire
Pennsylvania
West Virginia

13 LETTERS
North Carolina
South Carolina
Massachusetts

UNITED STATES OF AMERICA

GULF OF MEXICO

MASSACHUSETTS

NEW MEXICO

ILLINOIS

PENNSYLVANIA

NORTH DAKOTA

SOUTH CAROLINA

NORTH CAROLINA

MONTANA

ALASKA

NEW HAMPSHIRE

Answers on page 49.

SQUARE HUNT

Inside this big square are many smaller squares.
How many can you find altogether?

1 2 3 4 5 6 7 8 9
10 11 12 13 14
15 16 17 18
19 20 21
22 23
24 25
26 27

Answers on page 49.

Illustrated by Pat Me

THE SECRET LISTS

Webster and Wagnall both wanted the job of List Keeper to Queen Elistabeth. They each made a sample list. To keep their lists secret from one another, they each made up a code. Can you tell what's on each list and who wrote it?

goldfish

This is Webster's code:

A = N	J = W	S = F
B = O	K = X	T = G
C = P	L = Y	U = H
D = Q	M = Z	V = I
E = R	N = A	W = J
F = S	O = B	X = K
G = T	P = C	Y = L
H = U	Q = D	Z = M
I = V	R = E	

This is Wagnall's code:

A = Z	J = Q	S = H
B = Y	K = P	T = G
C = X	L = O	U = F
D = W	M = N	V = E
E = V	N = M	W = D
F = U	O = L	X = C
G = T	P = K	Y = B
H = S	Q = J	Z = A
I = R	R = I	

Sea Creatures

1. WRYYLSVFU
2. JUNYR
3. CBECBVFR
4. QBYCUVA
5. BPGBCHF
6. FRNUBEFR
7. FGNESVFU
8. FDHVQ

Vegetables

1. XZFORUOLDVI
2. YVVG
3. YVZM
4. XZIILG
5. OVGGFXV
6. YILXXLOR
7. XLIM
8. XVOVIB

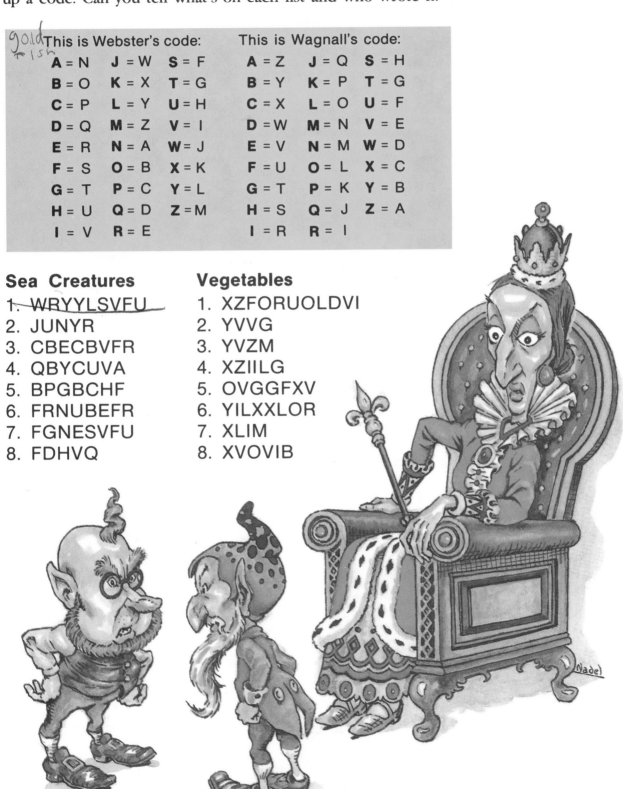

Answers on page 49.

Yo-Yo U.

These freshmen at Yo-Yo University were studying for their first big test when this happened. Can you tell which yo-yo belongs to each student?

Answers on page 49.

Illustrated by Barbara Gray

SOUR NOTES

How many things can you find wrong in this picture?

WORLD OF COLOR

These words are hidden in the letters you see below. Look up, down, sideways, backwards, and diagonally. Some letters are used more than once. When you find a word, circle it. After you finish, put the leftover letters in the blank spaces to spell a colorful message.

AQUA
PINK
BEIGE
PURPLE
BLACK
RED
BLUE
SHADE
BROWN
SHINY

COLOR WHEEL
SILVER
DARK
SPECTRUM
DULL
TAN
GOLD
TINT
GREEN
TRANSPARENT

GRAY
TURQUOISE
HUE
VIBRANT
ORCHID
VIOLET
LIGHT
WHITE
ORANGE
YELLOW

```
E  Y  E  L  L  O  W  A  L  T  R  S
T  R  A  N  S  P  A  R  E  N  T  P
I  A  E  I  N  Q  T  B  H  I  R  E
H  N  B  D  G  U  L  O  W  T  E  C
W  E  L  P  R  U  P  U  R  B  V  T
W  T  O  I  E  A  E  Y  E  E  L  R
V  H  R  N  E  O  A  O  O  I  I  U
I  G  C  K  N  R  W  K  R  G  S  M
O  I  H  E  N  G  A  R  O  E  D  D
L  L  I  F  C  B  L  A  C  K  L  U
E  O  D  L  S  H  A  D  E  O  O  L
T  U  R  Q  U  O  I  T  S  R  G  L
V  I  B  R  A  N  T  S  H  I  N  Y
```

Message:

____ _____ _____ _____ _____ _____ _____

Illustrated by Doug Taylor

PICKY'S PEACHES

Picky keeps his peach trees in perfect shape. In every row of trees, down, across, and diagonally, there are thirty peaches. Picky can tell how many peaches grow on each tree by the number of peaches on the corner trees. Can you?

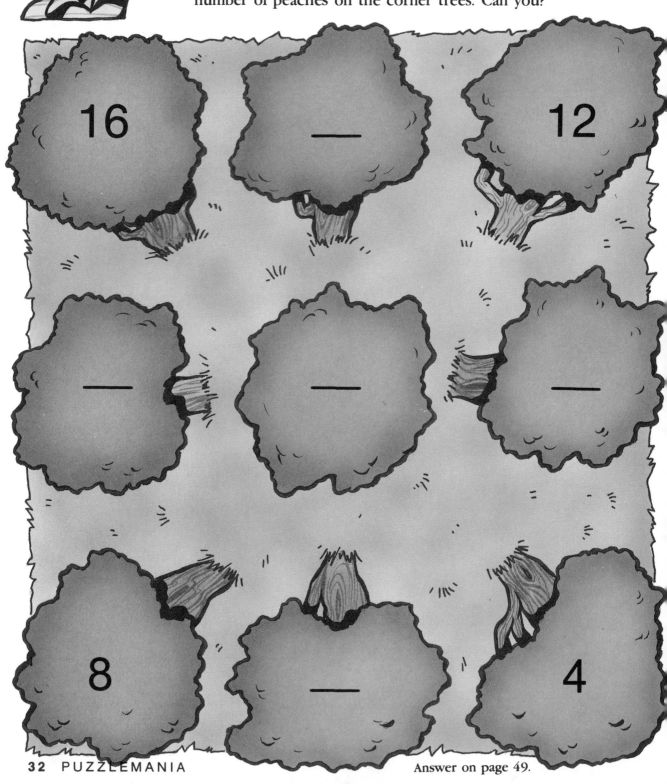

Answer on page 49.

ON THE GO

Look at these pictures. Write the words in the spaces next to them. When you finish, the letters in the yellow spaces will spell a long word. It means the way we move people and things from place to place.

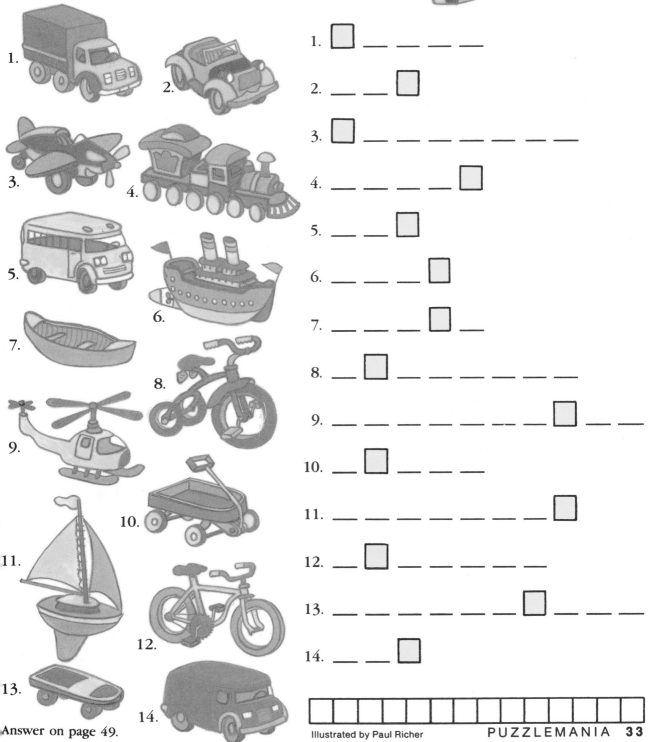

1. □ _ _ _ _

2. _ _ □

3. □ _ _ _ _ _ _

4. _ _ _ _ □

5. _ _ □

6. _ _ _ □

7. _ _ _ □ _

8. _ □ _ _ _ _ _

9. _ _ _ _ _ _ □ _ _

10. _ □ _ _ _

11. _ _ _ _ _ _ □

12. _ □ _ _ _ _ _

13. _ _ _ _ □ _ _ _

14. _ _ □

□□□□□□□□□□□□□

HIDDEN PICTURES

There are at least twenty objects hidden in this picture. How many can you find?

STACKING STUMPER

Mr. Stack, the lumberjack, has chopped a pile of wood.
Mr. Cross, his great big boss, said: "Straighten it up, if you could.
Put forty-five logs in every stack, and I will simply love it
If every row has one more log than the row above it."
How many logs in the bottom row?
That's what Mr. Stack needs to know.
Please help him figure out this mess.
Then turn to the answers and
check your guess.

Answers on page 50.

WHAT'S IN A WORD?

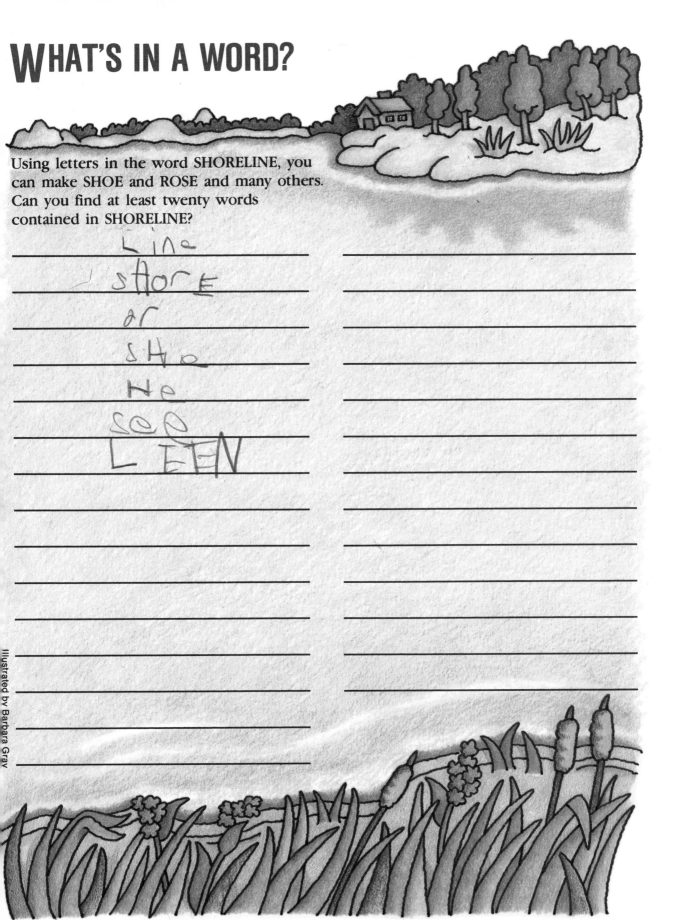

Using letters in the word SHORELINE, you can make SHOE and ROSE and many others. Can you find at least twenty words contained in SHORELINE?

Line
Shore
or
she
he
see
LEEN

Answers on page 50.

Illustrated by Barbara Gray

COMPUTER CRACK-UPS

Oops! Someone jiggled the giggle switch. Now the computer will do nothing but make riddles. Crack the coded answers and find out what's so funny.

Computer Code:

A = ☐	N = ⏢
B = ▲	O = ⋈
C = ▼	P = ↑
D = ♯	Q = ⊙
E = ∅	R = ⋈
F = ▲	S = ←
G = ■	T = ▽
H = ≠	U = ▭
I = ✕	V = ⊠
J = ▼	W = ▮▯
K = ▽	X = ⧓
L = ∞	Y = ♀♂
M = △	Z = →

1. What can speak every language?

□ ⏢   ∅ ▼ ≠ ⊠
A N   E C h O

2. What holds the moon up?

△ ⊠ ⊠ ⏢ ▲ ∅ □ △ ⇐
N O O N B E A N S

3. What is a pig after it is three days old?

▲ ⊠ ⊡ ⋈   # □ ∞ ⇐   ⊠ ∞ #
F O U g   D A Y S   O l D

4. Why did the crow sit on the telephone wire?

▽ ⊠   △ □ ▽ ∅   □
T O   M A K E   A

∞ ⊠ ⏢ ■   # ⅄ ⇐ ▽ □ ⏢ ▼ ∅
L O N G   D I S T A N C E

▼   □ ▣
C A W

Answers on page 50.

MEALTIME AT THE ZOO

When it's suppertime, the zoo keeper knows what everyone likes to eat. Can you match these animals with the foods they ask for in the poem that follows?

giraffe	elephant	seal	human	monkey
parrot	squirrel	rabbit	beaver	tiger

1. _____ I earn fresh fish for doing my tricks.

2. _____ I chew the bark off stacks of sticks.

3. _____ Hay helps my trunk grow very strong.

4. _____ I nibble bananas all the day long.

5. _____ A bowl of salad is dinner to me.

6. _____ I find my meals at the top of a tree.

7. _____ I like steak and many other meats.

8. _____ Acorns and nuts are my special treats.

9. _____ A pile of seeds fills up my belly.

10. _____ I munch on peanut butter and jelly!

Illustrated by Jerry Zimmerman

PUPPY PUZZLE

Cara, John, Ryan, and Diane have each chosen a puppy at the animal shelter. Look at the picture, and read the clues. Can you tell which puppy belongs to which child?

1. Diane didn't want a puppy with spots.

2. Ryan didn't choose a puppy with a collar.

3. John didn't pick a puppy that's sleeping.

4. Cara took a puppy that John and Diane did not want.

Illustrated by John Nez

Answers on page 50.

ALL ABOUT ANIMALS

How well do you know animals? Fill in the blanks and see.

1. Goldilocks visited the home of the three __ __ __ __ __.

2. Man's "best friend" is the __ __ __.

3. Little Boy Blue looked after __ __ __ __ __ and __ __ __ __.

4. Winnie-the-Pooh's friend Eeyore is a __ __ __ __ __ __ __.

5. Mary was followed to school by a little __ __ __ __.

6. Smokey the __ __ __ __ warns us about forest fires.

7. In a famous race a tortoise beat a __ __ __ __.

8. A red-nosed __ __ __ __ __ __ __ __ guides Santa's sleigh.

9. Three little __ __ __ __ __ __ __ lost their mittens.

10. A __ __ __ __ asked the Wizard of Oz for courage.

Answers on page 50.

STOP, LOOK, AND LIST

Under each category list one thing that begins with each letter. For example, one sport that begins with S is SOFTBALL. See if you can name another.

Sports

S _____

F _____

H _____

P _____

B _____

Pets

S _____

F _____

H _____

P _____

B _____

Musical Instruments

S _____

F _____

H _____

P _____

B _____

Answers on page 50.   Illustrated by Doug Taylor

OFF THE TOP OF YOUR HEAD

Use your imagination and finish drawing the costume contest winners.

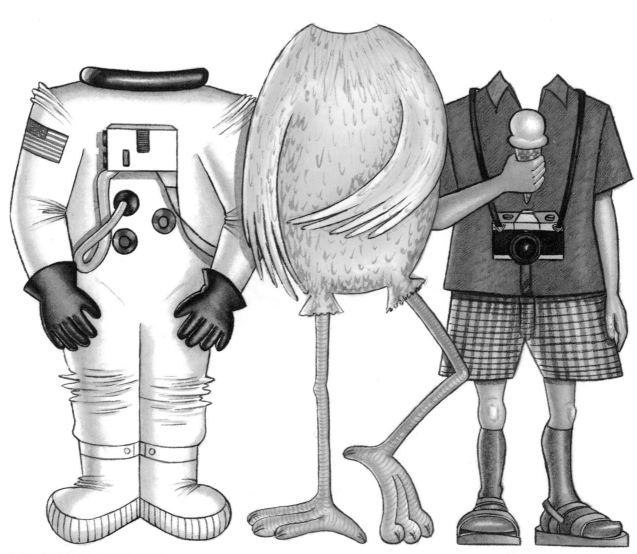

Illustrated by Jennifer Skopp

ROVING ROBOT

All the robots are in their places except the one in the center. Can you program its way to the empty corner?

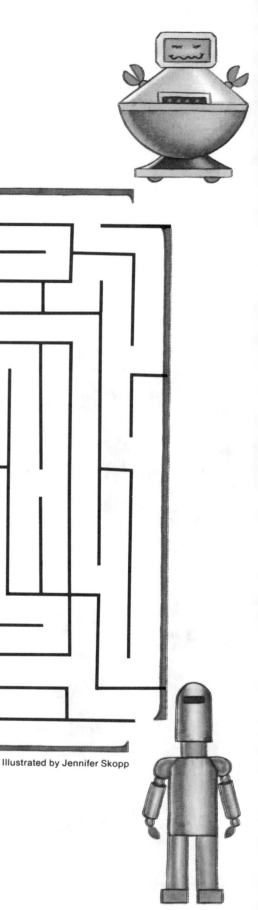

Finish

Start

Illustrated by Jennifer Skopp

Answer on page 50.